THIS JOURNAL BELONGS TO

Let this journal encourage you!

BROWN COUNSELING & CONSULTING, LLC

info.counselingandconsulting@gmail.com

monday

Date:

Daily affirmations

I AM _____
I AM _____
I AM _____
I AM _____

Grateful for

_____
_____
_____
_____

daily check in

I feel:

I need:

Inspiration:

Song:

WHAT I LIKE ABOUT MY SELF TODAY?

Word Of the Week

confident

THIS WEEK, HOW CAN I EMBODY THIS WORD?

_____
_____
_____
_____
_____
_____
_____
_____
_____

CONFIDENT

tuesday

Date:

Daily affirmations

I AM _____

I AM _____

I AM _____

I AM _____

Grateful for

_____
_____
_____
_____
_____

daily check in

I feel:

I need:

Inspiration:

Song:

WHAT I LIKE
ABOUT MY
SELF TODAY?

Word Of the Week

confident

HOW WOULD I DEFINE THIS WORD?

_____
_____
_____
_____
_____
_____
_____
_____
_____

CONFIDENT

wednesday

Date: _____

Daily affirmations

I AM _____
I AM _____
I AM _____
I AM _____

Grateful for

_____
_____
_____
_____
_____

daily check in

I feel:

I need:

Inspiration:

Song:

WHAT I LIKE ABOUT MY SELF TODAY?

Word Of the Week

confident

LIST WAYS I HAVE BEEN THIS WORD IN THE PAST AND PRESENT?

_____
_____
_____
_____
_____
_____
_____
_____
_____

CONFIDENT

thursday

Date:

Daily affirmations

I AM _____

I AM _____

I AM _____

I AM _____

Grateful for

_____

_____

_____

_____

_____

daily check in

I feel:

I need:

Inspiration:

Song:

WHAT I LIKE ABOUT MY SELF TODAY?

Word Of the Week

confident

WHO DO I KNOW IS THE BEST AT THIS? WHY?

_____

_____

_____

_____

_____

_____

_____

CONFIDENT

friday

Date:

Daily affirmations ———

I AM _____
I AM _____
I AM _____
I AM _____

Grateful for ———

_____
_____
_____
_____
_____

daily check in

I feel:

I need:

Inspiration:

Song:

WHAT I LIKE
ABOUT MY
SELF TODAY?

Word Of the Week

confident

WOULD MY FUTURE LOOK LIKE IF I DID MORE OF THIS
WORD EACH DAY?

_____
_____
_____
_____
_____
_____
_____
_____

CONFIDENT

weekend

Date: _____

Daily affirmations _____

I AM _____
I AM _____
I AM _____
I AM _____

Grateful for _____

_____
_____
_____
_____
_____

daily check in

I feel:

I need:

Inspiration:

Song:

WHAT I LIKE ABOUT MY SELF TODAY?

Word Of the Week

confident

REFLECTIONS

_____
_____
_____
_____
_____
_____
_____
_____
_____

CONFIDENT

Notes

monday

Date:

Daily affirmations

I AM _____

I AM _____

I AM _____

I AM _____

Grateful for

_____

_____

_____

_____

daily check in

I feel:

I need:

Inspiration:

Song:

WHAT I LIKE ABOUT MY SELF TODAY?

Word Of the Week —— **passionate** ——

THIS WEEK, HOW CAN I EMBODY THIS WORD?

_____

_____

_____

_____

_____

_____

_____

PASSIONATE

tuesday

Date:

Daily affirmations

I AM _____

I AM _____

I AM _____

I AM _____

Grateful for

_____

_____

_____

_____

daily check in

I feel:

I need:

Inspiration:

Song:

WHAT I LIKE ABOUT MY SELF TODAY?

Word Of the Week

passionate

HOW WOULD I DEFINE THIS WORD?

PASSIONATE

wednesday

Date: _____

Daily affirmations _____

I AM _____
I AM _____
I AM _____
I AM _____

Grateful for _____

_____
_____
_____
_____
_____

daily check in

I feel:

I need:

Inspiration:

Song:

WHAT I LIKE ABOUT MY SELF TODAY?

Word Of the Week

passionate

LIST WAYS I HAVE BEEN THIS WORD IN THE PAST AND PRESENT?

_____
_____
_____
_____
_____
_____
_____
_____
_____
_____
_____

PASSIONATE

thursday

Date:

Daily affirmations

I AM _____
I AM _____
I AM _____
I AM _____

Grateful for

_____
_____
_____
_____

daily check in

I feel:

I need:

Inspiration:

Song:

WHAT I LIKE ABOUT MY SELF TODAY?

Word Of the Week

passionate

WHO DO I KNOW IS THE BEST AT THIS? WHY?

_____
_____
_____
_____
_____
_____
_____
_____
_____
_____

PASSIONATE

friday

Date: _____

Daily affirmations _____

I AM _____
I AM _____
I AM _____
I AM _____

Grateful for _____

_____
_____
_____
_____
_____

daily check in

I feel:

I need:

Inspiration:

Song:

WHAT I LIKE
ABOUT MY
SELF TODAY?

Word Of the Week

_____ **passionate** _____

WHAT WOULD MY FUTURE LOOK LIKE IF I DID MORE OF
THIS WORD EACH DAY?

_____
_____
_____
_____
_____
_____
_____
_____
_____

PASSIONATE

weekend

Date:

Daily affirmations

I AM _____
I AM _____
I AM _____
I AM _____

Grateful for

_____
_____
_____
_____

daily check in

I feel:

I need:

Inspiration:

Song:

WHAT I LIKE
ABOUT MY
SELF TODAY?

Word Of the Week

passionate

REFLECTIONS

_____
_____
_____
_____
_____
_____
_____
_____
_____
_____

PASSIONATE

Notes

monday

Date:

Daily affirmations

I AM _____
I AM _____
I AM _____
I AM _____

Grateful for

_____
_____
_____
_____

daily check in

I feel:

I need:

Inspiration:

Song:

WHAT I LIKE
ABOUT MY
SELF TODAY?

Word Of the Week

innovative

THIS WEEK, HOW CAN I EMBODY THIS WORD?

_____
_____
_____
_____
_____
_____
_____
_____
_____

INNOVATIVE

tuesday

Date:

Daily affirmations

I AM _____

I AM _____

I AM _____

I AM _____

Grateful for

_____

_____

_____

_____

_____

daily check in

I feel:

I need:

Inspiration:

Song:

WHAT I LIKE ABOUT MY SELF TODAY?

Word Of the Week

innovative

HOW WOULD I DEFINE THIS WORD?

_____

_____

_____

_____

_____

_____

_____

_____

INNOVATIVE

wednesday

Date:

Daily affirmations

I AM _____
I AM _____
I AM _____
I AM _____

Grateful for

_____
_____
_____
_____

daily check in

I feel:

I need:

Inspiration:

Song:

WHAT I LIKE ABOUT MY SELF TODAY?

Word Of the Week

innovative

LIST WAYS I HAVE BEEN THIS WORD IN THE PAST AND PRESENT?

_____
_____
_____
_____
_____
_____
_____
_____

INNOVATIVE

thursday

Date:

Daily affirmations

I AM _____

I AM _____

I AM _____

I AM _____

Grateful for

_____

_____

_____

_____

daily check in

I feel:

I need:

Inspiration:

Song:

WHAT I LIKE
ABOUT MY
SELF TODAY?

Word Of the Week

innovative

WHO DO I KNOW THE BEST AT THIS? WHY?

_____

_____

_____

_____

_____

_____

_____

INNOVATIVE

friday

Date: _____

Daily affirmations

I AM _____
I AM _____
I AM _____
I AM _____

Grateful for

_____
_____
_____
_____
_____

daily check in

I feel:

I need:

Inspiration:

Song:

WHAT I LIKE ABOUT MY SELF TODAY?

Word Of the Week

innovative

WOULD MY FUTURE LOOK LIKE IF I DID MORE OF THIS WORD EACH DAY?

_____
_____
_____
_____
_____
_____
_____
_____

INNOVATIVE

weekend

Date:

Daily affirmations

I AM _____
I AM _____
I AM _____
I AM _____

Grateful for

_____
_____
_____
_____

daily check in

I feel:

I need:

Inspiration:

Song:

WHAT I LIKE
ABOUT MY
SELF TODAY?

Word
Of the
Week

innovative

REFLECTIONS

INNOVATIVE

Notes

monday

Date:

Daily affirmations

I AM _____

I AM _____

I AM _____

I AM _____

Grateful for

_____

_____

_____

_____

daily check in

I feel:

I need:

Inspiration:

Song:

WHAT I LIKE
ABOUT MY
SELF TODAY?

Word Of the Week

impactful

THIS WEEK, HOW CAN I EMBODY THIS WORD?

_____

_____

_____

_____

_____

_____

_____

_____

IMPACTFUL

tuesday

Date:

Daily affirmations

I AM _____
I AM _____
I AM _____
I AM _____

Grateful for

_____
_____
_____
_____

daily check in

I feel:

I need:

Inspiration:

Song:

WHAT I LIKE
ABOUT MY
SELF TODAY?

Word Of the Week

impactful

HOW WOULD I DEFINE THIS WORD?

_____
_____
_____
_____
_____
_____
_____
_____
_____

IMPACTFUL

wednesday

Date: _____

Daily affirmations

I AM _____
I AM _____
I AM _____
I AM _____

Grateful for

_____
_____
_____
_____

daily check in

I feel:

I need:

Inspiration:

Song:

WHAT I LIKE ABOUT MY SELF TODAY?

Word Of the Week

impactful

LIST WAYS I HAVE BEEN THIS WORD IN THE PAST AND PRESENT?

_____
_____
_____
_____
_____
_____
_____
_____
_____

IMPACTFUL

thursday

Date:

Daily affirmations

I AM _____
I AM _____
I AM _____
I AM _____

Grateful for

_____
_____
_____
_____
_____

daily check in

I feel:

I need:

Inspiration:

Song:

WHAT I LIKE ABOUT MY SELF TODAY?

Word Of the Week

impactful

WHO DO I KNOW IS BEST AT THIS? WHY?

_____
_____
_____
_____
_____
_____
_____
_____
_____

IMPACTFUL

friday

Date:

Daily affirmations

I AM _____
I AM _____
I AM _____
I AM _____

Grateful for

_____
_____
_____
_____
_____

daily check in

I feel:

I need:

Inspiration:

Song:

WHAT I LIKE ABOUT MY SELF TODAY?

Word Of the Week

impactful

WHAT WOULD MY FUTURE LOOK LIKE IF I DID MORE OF THIS WORD EACH DAY?

_____
_____
_____
_____
_____
_____
_____
_____
_____
_____
_____

IMPACTFUL

weekend

Date:

Daily affirmations

I AM _____
I AM _____
I AM _____
I AM _____

Grateful for

_____
_____
_____
_____

daily check in

I feel:

I need:

Inspiration:

Song:

WHAT I LIKE
ABOUT MY
SELF TODAY?

Word Of the Week

impactful

REFLECTIONS

_____
_____
_____
_____
_____
_____
_____
_____
_____

IMPACTFUL

Notes

monday

Date:

Daily affirmations

I AM _____
I AM _____
I AM _____
I AM _____

Grateful for

_____
_____
_____
_____

daily check in

I feel:

I need:

Inspiration:

Song:

WHAT I LIKE
ABOUT MY
SELF TODAY?

Word Of the Week

honoring

THIS WEEK, HOW CAN I EMBODY THIS WORD?

_____
_____
_____
_____
_____
_____
_____
_____
_____

HONORING

tuesday

Date:

Daily affirmations

I AM _____

I AM _____

I AM _____

I AM _____

Grateful for

_____

_____

_____

_____

daily check in

I feel:

I need:

Inspiration:

Song:

WHAT I LIKE ABOUT MY SELF TODAY?

Word Of the Week

honoring

HOW WOULD I DEFINE THIS WORD?

_____

_____

_____

_____

_____

_____

_____

_____

_____

HONORING

wednesday

Date:

Daily affirmations

I AM _____

I AM _____

I AM _____

I AM _____

Grateful for

_____

_____

_____

_____

daily check in

I feel:

I need:

Inspiration:

Song:

WHAT I LIKE ABOUT MY SELF TODAY?

Word Of the Week

honoring

LIST WAYS I HAVE BEEN THIS WORD IN THE PAST AND PRESENT?

_____

_____

_____

_____

_____

_____

_____

_____

_____

HONORING

thursday

Date:

Daily affirmations

I AM _____
I AM _____
I AM _____
I AM _____

Grateful for

_____
_____
_____
_____

daily check in

I feel:

I need:

Inspiration:

Song:

WHAT I LIKE ABOUT MY SELF TODAY?

Word Of the Week

honoring

WHO DO I KNOW IS THE BEST AT THIS? WHY?

_____
_____
_____
_____
_____
_____
_____
_____

HONORING

friday

Date:

Daily affirmations

I AM _____
I AM _____
I AM _____
I AM _____

Grateful for

_____
_____
_____
_____

daily check in

I feel:

I need:

Inspiration:

Song:

WHAT I LIKE
ABOUT MY
SELF TODAY?

Word Of the Week

honoring

WHAT WOULD MY FUTURE LOOK LIKE IF I DID MORE OF
THIS WORD EACH DAY?

_____
_____
_____
_____
_____
_____
_____
_____
_____

HONORING

weekend

Date:

Daily affirmations

I AM _____
I AM _____
I AM _____
I AM _____

Grateful for

_____
_____
_____
_____

daily check in

I feel:

I need:

Inspiration:

Song:

WHAT I LIKE
ABOUT MY
SELF TODAY?

Word Of the Week

honoring

REFLECTIONS

_____
_____
_____
_____
_____
_____
_____
_____

HONORING

Notes

monday

Date:

Daily affirmations

I AM _____

I AM _____

I AM _____

I AM _____

Grateful for

_____

_____

_____

_____

_____

daily check in

I feel:

I need:

Inspiration:

Song:

WHAT I LIKE
ABOUT MY
SELF TODAY?

Word Of the Week — authentic —

THIS WEEK, HOW CAN I EMBODY THIS WORD?

_____

_____

_____

_____

_____

_____

_____

AUTHENTIC

tuesday

Date:

Daily affirmations

I AM _____

I AM _____

I AM _____

I AM _____

Grateful for

_____

_____

_____

_____

daily check in

I feel:

I need:

Inspiration:

Song:

WHAT I LIKE ABOUT MY SELF TODAY?

Word Of the Week

authentic

HOW WOULD I DEFINE THIS WORD?

_____

_____

_____

_____

_____

_____

_____

_____

AUTHENTIC

wednesday

Date:

Daily affirmations

I AM _____
I AM _____
I AM _____
I AM _____

Grateful for

_____
_____
_____
_____
_____

daily check in

I feel:

I need:

Inspiration:

Song:

WHAT I LIKE
ABOUT MY
SELF TODAY?

Word Of the Week

authentic

LIST WAYS I HAVE BEEN THIS WORD IN THE PAST
AND PRESENT?

_____
_____
_____
_____
_____
_____
_____
_____
_____
_____

AUTHENTIC

thursday

Date:

Daily affirmations

I AM _____

I AM _____

I AM _____

I AM _____

Grateful for

_____

_____

_____

_____

_____

daily check in

I feel:

I need:

Inspiration:

Song:

WHAT I LIKE ABOUT MY SELF TODAY?

Word Of the Week

authentic

WHO DO I KNOW IS THE BEST AT THIS? WHY?

_____

_____

_____

_____

_____

_____

_____

_____

_____

AUTHENTIC

friday

Date:

Daily affirmations

I AM _____
I AM _____
I AM _____
I AM _____

Grateful for

_____
_____
_____
_____

daily check in

I feel:

I need:

Inspiration:

Song:

WHAT I LIKE
ABOUT MY
SELF TODAY?

Word Of the Week

authentic

WHAT WOULD MY FUTURE LOOK LIKE IF I DID MORE OF
THIS WORD EACH DAY?

_____
_____
_____
_____
_____
_____
_____
_____
_____

AUTHENTIC

weekend

Date:

Daily affirmations

I AM _____
I AM _____
I AM _____
I AM _____

Grateful for

_____
_____
_____
_____

daily check in

I feel:

I need:

Inspiration:

Song:

WHAT I LIKE
ABOUT MY
SELF TODAY?

Word Of the Week

authentic

REFLECTIONS

_____
_____
_____
_____
_____
_____
_____
_____

AUTHENTIC

Notes

_____
_____
_____
_____
_____
_____
_____
_____
_____
_____
_____
_____
_____
_____
_____
_____
_____
_____
_____
_____
_____
_____
_____
_____
_____
_____
_____
_____
_____

monday

Date:

Daily affirmations

I AM _____

I AM _____

I AM _____

I AM _____

Grateful for

_____

_____

_____

_____

daily check in

I feel:

I need:

Inspiration:

Song:

WHAT I LIKE
ABOUT MY
SELF TODAY?

Word Of the Week

perserverance

THIS WEEK, HOW CAN I EMBODY THIS WORD?

_____

_____

_____

_____

_____

_____

_____

_____

_____

PERSERVERANCE

tuesday

Date:

Daily affirmations

I AM _____
I AM _____
I AM _____
I AM _____

Grateful for

daily check in

I feel:

I need:

Inspiration:

Song:

WHAT I LIKE
ABOUT MY
SELF TODAY?

Word Of the Week

perserverance

HOW WOULD I DEFINE THIS WORD?

PERSERVERANCE

wednesday

Date:

Daily affirmations

I AM _____
I AM _____
I AM _____
I AM _____

Grateful for

_____
_____
_____
_____

daily check in

I feel:

I need:

Inspiration:

Song:

WHAT I LIKE ABOUT MY SELF TODAY?

Word Of the Week

_____ perserverance _____

LIST WAYS I HAVE BEEN THIS WORD IN THE PAST AND PRESENT?

_____
_____
_____
_____
_____
_____
_____
_____
_____
_____

PERSERVERANCE

thursday

Date: _____

Daily affirmations

I AM _____
I AM _____
I AM _____
I AM _____

Grateful for

_____
_____
_____
_____
_____

daily check in

I feel:

I need:

Inspiration:

Song:

WHAT I LIKE
ABOUT MY
SELF TODAY?

Word Of the Week

perserverance

THIS WEEK, HOW CAN I EMBODY THIS WORD?

_____
_____
_____
_____
_____
_____
_____
_____
_____

PERSERVERANCE

friday

Date: _____

Daily affirmations

I AM _____
I AM _____
I AM _____
I AM _____

Grateful for

_____
_____
_____
_____

daily check in

I feel:

I need:

Inspiration:

Song:

WHAT I LIKE
ABOUT MY
SELF TODAY?

Word Of the Week

perserverance

WHAT WOULD MY FUTURE LOOK LIKE IF I DID MORE OF
THIS WORD EACH DAY?

_____
_____
_____
_____
_____
_____
_____
_____
_____

PERSERVERANCE

weekend

Date: _____

Daily affirmations

I AM _____
I AM _____
I AM _____
I AM _____

Grateful for

_____
_____
_____
_____
_____

daily check in

I feel:

I need:

Inspiration:

Song:

WHAT I LIKE
ABOUT MY
SELF TODAY?

Word Of the Week

perserverance

REFLECTIONS

_____
_____
_____
_____
_____
_____
_____
_____
_____
_____

PERSERVERANCE

Notes

monday

Date:

Daily affirmations

I AM _____

I AM _____

I AM _____

I AM _____

Grateful for

_____
_____
_____
_____
_____

daily check in

I feel:

I need:

Inspiration:

Song:

WHAT I LIKE ABOUT MY SELF TODAY?

Word Of the Week

supporting

THIS WEEK, HOW CAN I EMBODY THIS WORD?

_____
_____
_____
_____
_____
_____
_____
_____
_____
_____

SUPPORTING

tuesday

Date:

Daily affirmations

I AM _____

I AM _____

I AM _____

I AM _____

Grateful for

_____

_____

_____

_____

_____

daily check in

I feel:

I need:

Inspiration:

Song:

WHAT I LIKE ABOUT MY SELF TODAY?

Word Of the Week

supporting

HOW WOULD I DEFINE THIS WORD?

_____

_____

_____

_____

_____

_____

_____

_____

SUPPORTING

wednesday

Date:

Daily affirmations

I AM _____

I AM _____

I AM _____

I AM _____

Grateful for

_____

_____

_____

_____

_____

daily check in

I feel:

I need:

Inspiration:

Song:

WHAT I LIKE
ABOUT MY
SELF TODAY?

Word Of the Week

supporting

LIST WAYS I HAVE BEEN THIS WORD IN THE PAST AND
PRESENT?

_____
_____
_____
_____
_____
_____
_____
_____
_____
_____

SUPPORTING

thursday

Date:

Daily affirmations

I AM _____

I AM _____

I AM _____

I AM _____

Grateful for

_____

_____

_____

_____

_____

daily check in

I feel:

I need:

Inspiration:

Song:

WHAT I LIKE
ABOUT MY
SELF TODAY?

Word Of the Week

supporting

WHO DO I KNOW IS THE BEST AT THIS? WHY?

_____

_____

_____

_____

_____

_____

_____

_____

SUPPORTING

friday

Date: _____

Daily affirmations

I AM _____
I AM _____
I AM _____
I AM _____

Grateful for

_____
_____
_____
_____

daily check in

I feel:

I need:

Inspiration:

Song:

WHAT I LIKE
ABOUT MY
SELF TODAY?

Word Of the Week

supporting

WHAT WOULD MY FUTURE LOOK LIKE IF I DID MORE OF
THIS WORD EACH DAY?

_____
_____
_____
_____
_____
_____
_____
_____
_____
_____

SUPPORTING

weekend

Date:

Daily affirmations

I AM _____
I AM _____
I AM _____
I AM _____

Grateful for

_____
_____
_____
_____
_____

daily check in

I feel:

I need:

Inspiration:

Song:

WHAT I LIKE
ABOUT MY
SELF TODAY?

Word Of the Week

supporting

REFLECTIONS

_____
_____
_____
_____
_____
_____
_____
_____
_____

SUPPORTING

Notes

monday

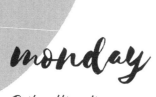

Date:

Daily affirmations

I AM _____
I AM _____
I AM _____
I AM _____

Grateful for

_____
_____
_____
_____
_____

daily check in

I feel:

I need:

Inspiration:

Song:

WHAT I LIKE ABOUT MY SELF TODAY?

Word Of the Week

powerful

THIS WEEK, HOW CAN I EMBODY THIS WORD?

_____
_____
_____
_____
_____
_____
_____
_____

POWERFUL

tuesday

Date:

Daily affirmations

I AM _____

I AM _____

I AM _____

I AM _____

Grateful for

_____

_____

_____

_____

_____

daily check in

I feel:

I need:

Inspiration:

Song:

WHAT I LIKE ABOUT MY SELF TODAY?

Word Of the Week

powerful

HOW WOULD I DEFINE THIS WORD?

_____

_____

_____

_____

_____

_____

_____

_____

POWERFUL

wednesday

Date:

Daily affirmations

I AM _____
I AM _____
I AM _____
I AM _____

Grateful for

_____
_____
_____
_____

daily check in

I feel:

I need:

Inspiration:

Song:

WHAT I LIKE
ABOUT MY
SELF TODAY?

Word Of the Week

powerful

LIST WAYS I HAVE BEEN THIS WORD IN THE PAST AND
PRESENT?

_____
_____
_____
_____
_____
_____
_____
_____
_____

POWERFUL

thursday

Date:

Daily affirmations

I AM _____
I AM _____
I AM _____
I AM _____

Grateful for

_____
_____
_____
_____

daily check in

I feel:

I need:

Inspiration:

Song:

WHAT I LIKE
ABOUT MY
SELF TODAY?

Word Of the Week

powerful

WHO DO YOU KNOW IS THE BEST AT THIS? WHY?

_____
_____
_____
_____
_____
_____
_____
_____

POWERFUL

friday

Date:

Daily affirmations

I AM _____

I AM _____

I AM _____

I AM _____

Grateful for

_____
_____
_____
_____

daily check in

I feel:

I need:

Inspiration:

Song:

WHAT I LIKE
ABOUT MY
SELF TODAY?

Word Of the Week

powerful

WHAT WOULD MY FUTURE LOOK LIKE IF I DID MORE OF
THIS WORD EACH DAY?

_____
_____
_____
_____
_____
_____
_____
_____
_____

POWERFUL

weekend

Date:

Daily affirmations

I AM _____

I AM _____

I AM _____

I AM _____

Grateful for

_____

_____

_____

_____

daily check in

I feel:

I need:

Inspiration:

Song:

WHAT I LIKE
ABOUT MY
SELF TODAY?

Word Of the Week

powerful
REFLECTIONS

_____

_____

_____

_____

_____

_____

_____

_____

POWERFUL

Notes

monday

Date:

Daily affirmations

I AM _____
I AM _____
I AM _____
I AM _____

Grateful for

_____
_____
_____
_____

daily check in

I feel:

I need:

Inspiration:

Song:

WHAT I LIKE ABOUT MY SELF TODAY?

Word Of the Week

successful

THIS WEEK, HOW CAN I EMBODY THIS WORD?

_____
_____
_____
_____
_____
_____
_____
_____

SUCCESSFUL

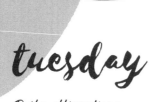

tuesday

Date:

Daily affirmations

I AM _____
I AM _____
I AM _____
I AM _____

Grateful for

_____
_____
_____
_____

daily check in

I feel:

I need:

Inspiration:

Song:

WHAT I LIKE ABOUT MY SELF TODAY?

Word Of the Week

successful

HOW WOULD I DEFINE THIS WORD?

_____
_____
_____
_____
_____
_____
_____
_____
_____

SUCCESSFUL

wednesday

Date:

Daily affirmations

I AM _____
I AM _____
I AM _____
I AM _____

Grateful for

_____
_____
_____
_____
_____

daily check in

I feel:

I need:

Inspiration:

Song:

WHAT I LIKE
ABOUT MY
SELF TODAY?

Word Of the Week

successful

LIST WAYS I HAVE BEEN THIS WORD IN THE PAST AND PRESENT?

_____
_____
_____
_____
_____
_____
_____
_____

SUCCESSFUL

thursday

Date:

Daily affirmations

I AM _____
I AM _____
I AM _____
I AM _____

Grateful for

_____
_____
_____
_____

daily check in

I feel:

I need:

Inspiration:

Song:

WHAT I LIKE ABOUT MY SELF TODAY?

Word Of the Week

successful

WHO DO YOU KNOW IS BEST AT THIS? WHY?

_____
_____
_____
_____
_____
_____
_____
_____

SUCCESSFUL

friday

Date:

Daily affirmations

I AM _____

I AM _____

I AM _____

I AM _____

Grateful for

_____

_____

_____

_____

_____

daily check in

I feel:

I need:

Inspiration:

Song:

WHAT I LIKE ABOUT MY SELF TODAY?

Word Of the Week

successful

WHAT WOULD MY FUTURE LOOK LIKE IF I DID MORE OF THIS WORD EACH DAY?

_____

_____

_____

_____

_____

_____

_____

_____

SUCCESSFUL

weekend

Date:

Daily affirmations

I AM _____
I AM _____
I AM _____
I AM _____

Grateful for

_____
_____
_____
_____
_____

daily check in

I feel:

I need:

Inspiration:

Song:

WHAT I LIKE
ABOUT MY
SELF TODAY?

Word
Of the
Week

successful
REFLECTIONS

_____
_____
_____
_____
_____
_____
_____
_____

SUCCESSFUL

Notes

monday

Date:

Daily affirmations

I AM _____
I AM _____
I AM _____
I AM _____

Grateful for

_____
_____
_____
_____
_____

daily check in

I feel:

I need:

Inspiration:

Song:

WHAT I LIKE
ABOUT MY
SELF TODAY?

Word Of the Week

jubilant

THIS WEEK, HOW CAN I EMBODY THIS WORD?

_____
_____
_____
_____
_____
_____
_____
_____

JUBLIANT

tuesday

Date:

Daily affirmations

I AM _____

I AM _____

I AM _____

I AM _____

Grateful for

_____

_____

_____

_____

_____

daily check in

I feel:

I need:

Inspiration:

Song:

WHAT I LIKE
ABOUT MY
SELF TODAY?

Word Of the Week

jubilant

HOW WOULD YOU DEFINE THIS WORD?

_____

_____

_____

_____

_____

_____

_____

_____

JUBLIANT

wednesday

Date:

Daily affirmations

I AM _____

I AM _____

I AM _____

I AM _____

Grateful for

_____

_____

_____

_____

_____

daily check in

I feel:

I need:

Inspiration:

Song:

WHAT I LIKE ABOUT MY SELF TODAY?

Word Of the Week

jubilant

LIST WAYS I HAVE BEEN THIS WORD IN THE PAST AND PRESENT?

_____

_____

_____

_____

_____

_____

_____

_____

_____

JUBLIANT

thursday

Date: _____

Daily affirmations

I AM _____
I AM _____
I AM _____
I AM _____

Grateful for

_____
_____
_____
_____

daily check in

I feel:

I need:

Inspiration:

Song:

WHAT I LIKE
ABOUT MY
SELF TODAY?

Word Of the Week

jubilant

WHO DO I KNOW IS BEST AT THIS? WHY?

_____
_____
_____
_____
_____
_____
_____
_____
_____

JUBLIANT

friday

Date: _____

Daily affirmations

I AM _____
I AM _____
I AM _____
I AM _____

Grateful for

_____
_____
_____
_____
_____

daily check in

I feel:

I need:

Inspiration:

Song:

WHAT I LIKE ABOUT MY SELF TODAY?

Word Of the Week

jubilant

WHAT WOULD MY FUTURE LOOK LIKE IF I DID MORE OF THIS WORD EACH DAY?

_____
_____
_____
_____
_____
_____
_____
_____

JUBLIANT

weekend

Date:

Daily affirmations

I AM _____
I AM _____
I AM _____
I AM _____

Grateful for

daily check in

I feel:

I need:

Inspiration:

Song:

WHAT I LIKE
ABOUT MY
SELF TODAY?

Word Of the Week

jubilant

REFLECTIONS

JUBLIANT

Notes

monday

Date:

Daily affirmations

I AM _____
I AM _____
I AM _____
I AM _____

Grateful for

_____
_____
_____
_____

daily check in

I feel:

I need:

Inspiration:

Song:

WHAT I LIKE ABOUT MY SELF TODAY?

Word Of the Week

unbreakable

THIS WEEK, HOW CAN I EMBODY THIS WORD?

_____
_____
_____
_____
_____
_____
_____

UNBREAKABLE

tuesday

Date:

Daily affirmations

I AM _____

I AM _____

I AM _____

I AM _____

Grateful for

_____

_____

_____

_____

_____

daily check in

I feel:

I need:

Inspiration:

Song:

WHAT I LIKE ABOUT MY SELF TODAY?

Word Of the Week

unbreakable

HOW WOULD I DEFINE THIS WORD?

_____

_____

_____

_____

_____

_____

_____

_____

UNBREAKABLE

wednesday

Date: _____

Daily affirmations

I AM _____

I AM _____

I AM _____

I AM _____

Grateful for

_____

_____

_____

_____

_____

daily check in

I feel:

I need:

Inspiration:

Song:

WHAT I LIKE ABOUT MY SELF TODAY?

Word Of the Week

unbreakable

LIST WAYS I HAVE BEEN THIS WORD IN THE PAST AND PRESENT?

_____

_____

_____

_____

_____

_____

_____

_____

_____

_____

UNBREAKABLE

thursday

Date:

Daily affirmations

I AM _____
I AM _____
I AM _____
I AM _____

Grateful for

_____
_____
_____
_____

daily check in

I feel:

I need:

Inspiration:

Song:

WHAT I LIKE ABOUT MY SELF TODAY?

Word Of the Week

unbreakable

WHO DO YOU KNOW IS THE BEST AT THIS? WHY?

_____
_____
_____
_____
_____
_____
_____
_____

UNBREAKABLE

friday

Date:

Daily affirmations

I AM _____
I AM _____
I AM _____
I AM _____

Grateful for

_____
_____
_____
_____

daily check in

I feel:

I need:

Inspiration:

Song:

WHAT I LIKE
ABOUT MY
SELF TODAY?

Word Of the Week

unbreakable

WHAT WOULD MY FUTURE LOOK LIKE IF I DID MORE OF
THIS WORD EACH DAY?

_____
_____
_____
_____
_____
_____
_____
_____

UNBREAKABLE

weekend

Date:

Daily affirmations

I AM _____
I AM _____
I AM _____
I AM _____

Grateful for

_____
_____
_____
_____

daily check in

I feel:

I need:

Inspiration:

Song:

WHAT I LIKE ABOUT MY SELF TODAY?

Word Of the Week

unbreakable

REFLECTIONS

_____
_____
_____
_____
_____
_____
_____
_____
_____
_____

UNBREAKABLE

Notes

monday

Date: _____

Daily affirmations

I AM _____
I AM _____
I AM _____
I AM _____

Grateful for

_____
_____
_____
_____
_____

daily check in

I feel:

I need:

Inspiration:

Song:

WHAT I LIKE ABOUT MY SELF TODAY?

Word Of the Week — dedicated

THIS WEEK, HOW CAN I EMBODY THIS WORD?

_____
_____
_____
_____
_____
_____
_____
_____

DEDICATED

tuesday

Date:

Daily affirmations

I AM _____
I AM _____
I AM _____
I AM _____

Grateful for

_____
_____
_____
_____

daily check in

I feel:

I need:

Inspiration:

Song:

WHAT I LIKE ABOUT MY SELF TODAY?

Word Of the Week

dedicated

HOW WOULD I DEFINE THIS WORD?

_____
_____
_____
_____
_____
_____
_____

DEDICATED

wednesday

Date:

Daily affirmations

I AM _____
I AM _____
I AM _____
I AM _____

Grateful for

_____
_____
_____
_____
_____

daily check in

I feel:

I need:

Inspiration:

Song:

WHAT I LIKE ABOUT MY SELF TODAY?

Word Of the Week

dedicated

LIST WAYS I HAVE BEEN THIS WORD IN THE PAST AND PRESENT?

_____
_____
_____
_____
_____
_____
_____
_____

DEDICATED

thursday

Date:

Daily affirmations

I AM _____
I AM _____
I AM _____
I AM _____

Grateful for

_____
_____
_____
_____
_____

daily check in

I feel:

I need:

Inspiration:

Song:

WHAT I LIKE ABOUT MY SELF TODAY?

Word Of the Week

dedicated

WHO DO I KNOW IS BEST AT THIS? WHY?

_____
_____
_____
_____
_____
_____
_____
_____

DEDICATED

friday

Date:

Daily affirmations

I AM _____

I AM _____

I AM _____

I AM _____

Grateful for

_____

_____

_____

_____

daily check in

I feel:

I need:

Inspiration:

Song:

WHAT I LIKE ABOUT MY SELF TODAY?

Word Of the Week

dedicated

WHAT WOULD MY FUTURE LOOK LIKE IF I DID MORE OF THIS WORD EACH DAY?

_____

_____

_____

_____

_____

_____

_____

_____

DEDICATED

weekend

Date:

Daily affirmations

I AM _____
I AM _____
I AM _____
I AM _____

Grateful for

_____
_____
_____
_____

daily check in

I feel:

I need:

Inspiration:

Song:

WHAT I LIKE
ABOUT MY
SELF TODAY?

Word Of the Week

dedicated

REFLECTIONS

_____
_____
_____
_____
_____
_____
_____
_____
_____
_____
_____

DEDICATED

Notes

monday

Date:

Daily affirmations

I AM _____

I AM _____

I AM _____

I AM _____

Grateful for

_____

_____

_____

_____

_____

daily check in

I feel:

I need:

Inspiration:

Song:

WHAT I LIKE ABOUT MY SELF TODAY?

Word Of the Week

worthy

THIS WEEK, HOW CAN I EMBODY THIS WORD?

_____

_____

_____

_____

_____

_____

_____

_____

_____

WORTHY

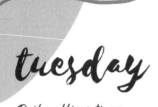

tuesday

Date:

Daily affirmations

I AM _____
I AM _____
I AM _____
I AM _____

Grateful for

_____
_____
_____
_____

daily check in

I feel:

I need:

Inspiration:

Song:

WHAT I LIKE
ABOUT MY
SELF TODAY?

Word Of the Week

worthy

HOW WOULD I DEFINE THIS WORD?

_____
_____
_____
_____
_____
_____
_____
_____

WORTHY

wednesday

Date:

Daily affirmations

I AM _____
I AM _____
I AM _____
I AM _____

Grateful for

_____
_____
_____
_____
_____

daily check in

I feel:

I need:

Inspiration:

Song:

WHAT I LIKE ABOUT MY SELF TODAY?

Word Of the Week

worthy

LIST WAYS I HAVE BEEN THIS WORD IN THE PAST AND PRESENT?

_____
_____
_____
_____
_____
_____
_____
_____
_____
_____

WORTHY

thursday

Date:

Daily affirmations

I AM _____
I AM _____
I AM _____
I AM _____

Grateful for

_____
_____
_____
_____

daily check in

I feel:

I need:

Inspiration:

Song:

WHAT I LIKE
ABOUT MY
SELF TODAY?

Word Of the Week

worthy

WHO DO I KNOW IS BEST AT THIS? WHY?

_____
_____
_____
_____
_____
_____
_____
_____

WORTHY

friday

Date: _____

Daily affirmations

I AM _____
I AM _____
I AM _____
I AM _____

Grateful for

_____
_____
_____
_____

daily check in

I feel:

I need:

Inspiration:

Song:

WHAT I LIKE ABOUT MY SELF TODAY?

Word Of the Week

worthy

WHAT WOULD MY FUTURE LOOK LIKE IF I DID MORE OF THIS WORD EACH DAY?

_____
_____
_____
_____
_____
_____
_____
_____
_____

WORTHY

weekend

Date:

Daily affirmations

I AM _____
I AM _____
I AM _____
I AM _____

Grateful for

_____
_____
_____
_____
_____

daily check in

I feel:

I need:

Inspiration:

Song:

WHAT I LIKE
ABOUT MY
SELF TODAY?

Word Of the Week

worthy

REFLECTIONS

_____
_____
_____
_____
_____
_____
_____
_____
_____

WORTHY

Notes

monday

Date:

Daily affirmations

I AM _____
I AM _____
I AM _____
I AM _____

Grateful for

_____
_____
_____
_____

daily check in

I feel:

I need:

Inspiration:

Song:

WHAT I LIKE
ABOUT MY
SELF TODAY?

Word Of the Week

happy

THIS WEEK, HOW CAN I EMBODY THIS WORD?

_____
_____
_____
_____
_____
_____
_____
_____

HAPPY

tuesday

Date:

Daily affirmations

I AM _____
I AM _____
I AM _____
I AM _____

Grateful for

_____
_____
_____
_____

daily check in

I feel:

I need:

Inspiration:

Song:

WHAT I LIKE ABOUT MY SELF TODAY?

Word Of the Week

happy

HOW WOULD I DEFINE THIS WORD?

_____
_____
_____
_____
_____
_____
_____
_____

HAPPY

wednesday

Date:

Daily affirmations

I AM _____

I AM _____

I AM _____

I AM _____

Grateful for

_____

_____

_____

_____

daily check in

I feel:

I need:

Inspiration:

Song:

WHAT I LIKE ABOUT MY SELF TODAY?

Word Of the Week

happy

LIST WAYS I HAVE BEEN THIS WORD IN THE PAST AND PRESENT?

_____

_____

_____

_____

_____

_____

_____

_____

_____

_____

HAPPY

thursday

Date:

Daily affirmations

I AM _____
I AM _____
I AM _____
I AM _____

Grateful for

_____
_____
_____
_____

daily check in

I feel:

I need:

Inspiration:

Song:

WHAT I LIKE
ABOUT MY
SELF TODAY?

Word
Of the
Week

happy

WHO DO YOU KNOW IS THE BEST AT THIS? WHY?

_____
_____
_____
_____
_____
_____
_____
_____
_____

HAPPY

friday

Date:

Daily affirmations

I AM _____

I AM _____

I AM _____

I AM _____

Grateful for

_____
_____
_____
_____

daily check in

I feel:

I need:

Inspiration:

Song:

WHAT I LIKE ABOUT MY SELF TODAY?

Word Of the Week

happy

WHAT WOULD MY FUTURE LOOK LIKE IF I DID MORE OF THIS WORD EACH DAY?

_____
_____
_____
_____
_____
_____
_____
_____
_____
_____

HAPPY

weekend

Date: _____

Daily affirmations _____

I AM _____
I AM _____
I AM _____
I AM _____

Grateful for _____

_____
_____
_____
_____
_____

daily check in

I feel:

I need:

Inspiration:

Song:

WHAT I LIKE
ABOUT MY
SELF TODAY?

Word Of the Week

happy
REFLECTIONS

_____
_____
_____
_____
_____
_____
_____
_____
_____
_____
_____

HAPPY

Notes

monday

Date:

Daily affirmations

I AM _____
I AM _____
I AM _____
I AM _____

Grateful for

_____
_____
_____
_____
_____

daily check in

I feel:

I need:

Inspiration:

Song:

WHAT I LIKE ABOUT MY SELF TODAY?

Word Of the Week

insightful

THIS WEEK, HOW CAN I EMBODY THIS WORD?

_____
_____
_____
_____
_____
_____
_____
_____
_____
_____

INSIGHTFUL

tuesday

Date:

Daily affirmations

I AM _____

I AM _____

I AM _____

I AM _____

Grateful for

_____

_____

_____

_____

daily check in

I feel:

I need:

Inspiration:

Song:

WHAT I LIKE
ABOUT MY
SELF TODAY?

Word Of the Week

insightful

HOW WOULD I DEFINE THIS WORD?

_____

_____

_____

_____

_____

_____

_____

_____

_____

INSIGHTFUL

wednesday

Date:

Daily affirmations

I AM _____
I AM _____
I AM _____
I AM _____

Grateful for

_____
_____
_____
_____

daily check in

I feel:

I need:

Inspiration:

Song:

WHAT I LIKE ABOUT MY SELF TODAY?

Word Of the Week

insightful

LIST WAYS I HAVE BEEN THIS WORD IN THE PAST AND PRESENT?

_____
_____
_____
_____
_____
_____
_____
_____
_____
_____
_____

INSIGHTFUL

thursday

Date:

Daily affirmations

I AM _____
I AM _____
I AM _____
I AM _____

Grateful for

_____
_____
_____
_____

daily check in

I feel:

I need:

Inspiration:

Song:

WHAT I LIKE
ABOUT MY
SELF TODAY?

Word Of the Week

insightful

WHO DO I KNOW IS THE BEST AT THIS? WHY?

_____
_____
_____
_____
_____
_____
_____
_____
_____

INSIGHTFUL

friday

Date:

Daily affirmations

I AM _____
I AM _____
I AM _____
I AM _____

Grateful for

_____
_____
_____
_____
_____

daily check in

I feel:

I need:

Inspiration:

Song:

WHAT I LIKE ABOUT MY SELF TODAY?

Word Of the Week

insightful

WHAT WOULD MY FUTURE LOOK LIKE IF I DID MORE OF THIS WORD EACH DAY?

_____
_____
_____
_____
_____
_____
_____
_____

INSIGHTFUL

weekend

Date:

Daily affirmations

I AM _____
I AM _____
I AM _____
I AM _____

Grateful for

_____
_____
_____
_____
_____

daily check in

I feel:

I need:

Inspiration:

Song:

WHAT I LIKE
ABOUT MY
SELF TODAY?

Word Of the Week

insightful

REFLECTIONS

_____
_____
_____
_____
_____
_____
_____
_____
_____

INSIGHTFUL

Notes

monday

Date:

Daily affirmations

I AM _____

I AM _____

I AM _____

I AM _____

Grateful for

_____

_____

_____

_____

daily check in

I feel:

I need:

Inspiration:

Song:

WHAT I LIKE ABOUT MY SELF TODAY?

Word Of the Week

effective

THIS WEEK, HOW CAN I EMBODY THIS WORD?

_____

_____

_____

_____

_____

_____

_____

_____

_____

EFFECTIVE

tuesday

Date:

Daily affirmations

I AM _____
I AM _____
I AM _____
I AM _____

Grateful for

_____
_____
_____
_____

daily check in

I feel:

I need:

Inspiration:

Song:

WHAT I LIKE
ABOUT MY
SELF TODAY?

Word Of the Week

effective

HOW WOULD I DEFINE THIS WORD?

_____
_____
_____
_____
_____
_____
_____
_____

EFFECTIVE

wednesday

Date:

Daily affirmations

I AM _____
I AM _____
I AM _____
I AM _____

Grateful for

_____
_____
_____
_____

daily check in

I feel:

I need:

Inspiration:

Song:

WHAT I LIKE ABOUT MY SELF TODAY?

Word Of the Week

effective

LIST WAYS I HAVE BEEN THIS WORD IN THE PAST AND PRESENT?

_____
_____
_____
_____
_____
_____
_____
_____
_____

EFFECTIVE

thursday

Date: _____

Daily affirmations _____

I AM _____
I AM _____
I AM _____
I AM _____

Grateful for _____

_____
_____
_____
_____

daily check in

I feel:

I need:

Inspiration:

Song:

WHAT I LIKE ABOUT MY SELF TODAY?

Word Of the Week

effective

WHO DO I KNOW IS THE BEST AT THIS? WHY?

_____
_____
_____
_____
_____
_____
_____
_____
_____
_____
_____

EFFECTIVE

friday

Date: _____

Daily affirmations _____

I AM _____
I AM _____
I AM _____
I AM _____

Grateful for _____

_____
_____
_____
_____

daily check in

I feel:

I need:

Inspiration:

Song:

WHAT I LIKE
ABOUT MY
SELF TODAY?

Word Of the Week

effective

WHAT WOULD MY FUTURE LOOK LIKE IF I DID MORE OF
THIS WORD EACH DAY?

_____
_____
_____
_____
_____
_____
_____
_____
_____

EFFECTIVE

weekend

Date:

Daily affirmations

I AM _____
I AM _____
I AM _____
I AM _____

Grateful for

_____
_____
_____
_____

daily check in

I feel:

I need:

Inspiration:

Song:

WHAT I LIKE
ABOUT MY
SELF TODAY?

Word Of the Week

effective

REFLECTIONS

_____
_____
_____
_____
_____
_____
_____
_____

EFFECTIVE

Notes

monday

Date:

Daily affirmations

I AM _____

I AM _____

I AM _____

I AM _____

Grateful for

_____

_____

_____

_____

daily check in

I feel:

I need:

Inspiration:

Song:

WHAT I LIKE
ABOUT MY
SELF TODAY?

Word Of the Week

unique

THIS WEEK, HOW CAN I EMBODY THIS WORD?

_____

_____

_____

_____

_____

_____

_____

_____

UNIQUE

tuesday

Date:

Daily affirmations

I AM _____
I AM _____
I AM _____
I AM _____

Grateful for

_____
_____
_____
_____
_____

daily check in

I feel:

I need:

Inspiration:

Song:

WHAT I LIKE ABOUT MY SELF TODAY?

Word Of the Week

unique

HOW WOULD I DEFINE THIS WORD?

_____
_____
_____
_____
_____
_____
_____
_____
_____
_____

UNIQUE

wednesday

Date: _____

Daily affirmations _____

I AM _____
I AM _____
I AM _____
I AM _____

Grateful for _____

_____
_____
_____
_____
_____

daily check in

I feel:

I need:

Inspiration:

Song:

WHAT I LIKE ABOUT MY SELF TODAY?

Word Of the Week _____

unique

LIST WAYS I HAVE BEEN THIS WORD IN THE PAST AND PRESENT?

_____
_____
_____
_____
_____
_____
_____
_____

UNIQUE

thursday

Date: _____

Daily affirmations

I AM _____
I AM _____
I AM _____
I AM _____

Grateful for

_____
_____
_____
_____
_____

daily check in

I feel:

I need:

Inspiration:

Song:

WHAT I LIKE
ABOUT MY
SELF TODAY?

Word Of the Week

unique

WHO DO I KNOW IS THE BEST AT THIS? WHY?

_____
_____
_____
_____
_____
_____
_____
_____
_____

UNIQUE

friday

Date: _____

Daily affirmations _____

I AM _____
I AM _____
I AM _____
I AM _____

Grateful for _____

_____
_____
_____
_____
_____

daily check in

I feel:

I need:

Inspiration:

Song:

WHAT I LIKE ABOUT MY SELF TODAY?

Word Of the Week

unique

WHAT WOULD MY FUTURE LOOK LIKE IF I DID MORE OF THIS WORD EACH DAY?

_____
_____
_____
_____
_____
_____
_____
_____
_____

UNIQUE

weekend

Date:

Daily affirmations

I AM _____
I AM _____
I AM _____
I AM _____

Grateful for

_____
_____
_____
_____
_____

daily check in

I feel:

I need:

Inspiration:

Song:

WHAT I LIKE
ABOUT MY
SELF TODAY?

Word Of the Week

unique

REFLECTIONS

_____
_____
_____
_____
_____
_____
_____
_____
_____
_____

UNIQUE

Notes

monday

Date:

Daily affirmations

I AM _____

I AM _____

I AM _____

I AM _____

Grateful for

_____

_____

_____

_____

_____

daily check in

I feel:

I need:

Inspiration:

Song:

WHAT I LIKE
ABOUT MY
SELF TODAY?

Word Of the Week

deserving

THIS WEEK, HOW CAN I EMBODY THIS WORD?

_____

_____

_____

_____

_____

_____

_____

_____

DESERVING

tuesday

Date:

Daily affirmations

I AM _____
I AM _____
I AM _____
I AM _____

Grateful for

_____
_____
_____
_____
_____

daily check in

I feel:

I need:

Inspiration:

Song:

WHAT I LIKE
ABOUT MY
SELF TODAY?

Word Of the Week

deserving

HOW WOULD I DEFINE THIS WORD?

_____
_____
_____
_____
_____
_____
_____
_____
_____

DESERVING

wednesday

Date:

Daily affirmations

I AM _____

I AM _____

I AM _____

I AM _____

Grateful for

_____

_____

_____

_____

daily check in

I feel:

I need:

Inspiration:

Song:

WHAT I LIKE
ABOUT MY
SELF TODAY?

Word Of the Week

deserving

LIST WAYS I HAVE BEEN THIS WORD IN THE PAST AND
PRESENT?

_____

_____

_____

_____

_____

_____

_____

_____

_____

_____

DESERVING

thursday

Date:

Daily affirmations

I AM _____

I AM _____

I AM _____

I AM _____

Grateful for

_____

_____

_____

_____

daily check in

I feel:

I need:

Inspiration:

Song:

WHAT I LIKE
ABOUT MY
SELF TODAY?

Word Of the Week

deserving

WHO WOULD I SAY IS THE BEST AT THIS? WHY?

_____

_____

_____

_____

_____

_____

_____

_____

_____

DESERVING

friday

Date:

Daily affirmations

I AM _____
I AM _____
I AM _____
I AM _____

Grateful for

_____
_____
_____
_____
_____

daily check in

I feel:

I need:

Inspiration:

Song:

WHAT I LIKE ABOUT MY SELF TODAY?

Word Of the Week

deserving

WHAT WOULD MY FUTURE LOOK LIKE IF I DID MORE OF THIS WORD EACH DAY?

_____
_____
_____
_____
_____
_____
_____
_____
_____
_____

DESERVING

weekend

Date:

Daily affirmations

I AM _____
I AM _____
I AM _____
I AM _____

Grateful for

_____
_____
_____
_____
_____

daily check in

I feel:

I need:

Inspiration:

Song:

WHAT I LIKE
ABOUT MY
SELF TODAY?

Word Of the Week

deserving
REFLECTIONS

_____
_____
_____
_____
_____
_____
_____
_____
_____
_____

DESERVING

Notes

monday

Date:

Daily affirmations

I AM _____

I AM _____

I AM _____

I AM _____

Grateful for

_____

_____

_____

_____

daily check in

I feel:

I need:

Inspiration:

Song:

WHAT I LIKE
ABOUT MY
SELF TODAY?

Word Of the Week

loveable

REFLECTIONS

_____

_____

_____

_____

_____

_____

_____

_____

_____

_____

LOVEABLE

tuesday

Date:

Daily affirmations

I AM _____

I AM _____

I AM _____

I AM _____

Grateful for

_____
_____
_____
_____

daily check in

I feel:

I need:

Inspiration:

Song:

WHAT I LIKE ABOUT MY SELF TODAY?

Word Of the Week

loveable

HOW WOULD YOU DEFINE THIS WORD?

_____
_____
_____
_____
_____
_____
_____
_____
_____

LOVEABLE

wednesday

Date:

Daily affirmations

I AM _____

I AM _____

I AM _____

I AM _____

Grateful for

_____

_____

_____

_____

_____

daily check in

I feel:

I need:

Inspiration:

Song:

WHAT I LIKE
ABOUT MY
SELF TODAY?

Word Of the Week

loveable

LIST WAYS I HAVE BEEN THIS WORD IN THE PAST AND
PRESENT?

_____

_____

_____

_____

_____

_____

_____

_____

_____

_____

LOVEABLE

thursday

Date:

Daily affirmations

I AM _____
I AM _____
I AM _____
I AM _____

Grateful for

_____
_____
_____
_____

daily check in

I feel:

I need:

Inspiration:

Song:

WHAT I LIKE
ABOUT MY
SELF TODAY?

Word Of the Week

loveable

WHO DO I KNOW IS THE BEST AT THIS? WHY?

_____
_____
_____
_____
_____
_____
_____
_____
_____
_____

LOVEABLE

friday

Date:

Daily affirmations

I AM _____

I AM _____

I AM _____

I AM _____

Grateful for

_____
_____
_____
_____
_____

daily check in

I feel:

I need:

Inspiration:

Song:

WHAT I LIKE
ABOUT MY
SELF TODAY?

Word Of the Week

loveable

WHAT WOULD MY FUTURE LOOK LIKE IF I DID MORE OF
THIS WORD EACH DAY?

_____
_____
_____
_____
_____
_____
_____
_____
_____
_____

LOVEABLE

weekend

Date:

Daily affirmations

I AM _____

I AM _____

I AM _____

I AM _____

Grateful for

_____

_____

_____

_____

daily check in

I feel:

I need:

Inspiration:

Song:

WHAT I LIKE
ABOUT MY
SELF TODAY?

Word Of the Week

loveable

REFLECTIONS

LOVEABLE

Notes

monday

Date:

Daily affirmations

I AM _____

I AM _____

I AM _____

I AM _____

Grateful for

_____

_____

_____

_____

_____

daily check in

I feel:

I need:

Inspiration:

Song:

WHAT I LIKE ABOUT MY SELF TODAY?

Word Of the Week

active

THIS WEEK, HOW CAN I EMBODY THIS WORD?

_____

_____

_____

_____

_____

_____

_____

_____

_____

_____

ACTIVE

tuesday

Date:

Daily affirmations

I AM _____

I AM _____

I AM _____

I AM _____

Grateful for

_____

_____

_____

_____

_____

daily check in

I feel:

I need:

Inspiration:

Song:

WHAT I LIKE ABOUT MY SELF TODAY?

Word Of the Week

active

HOW WOULD I DEFINE THIS WORD?

ACTIVE

wednesday

Date:

Daily affirmations

I AM _____
I AM _____
I AM _____
I AM _____

Grateful for

_____
_____
_____
_____

daily check in

I feel:

I need:

Inspiration:

Song:

WHAT I LIKE ABOUT MY SELF TODAY?

Word Of the Week

active

LIST WAYS I HAVE BEEN THIS WORD IN THE PAST AND PRESENT?

_____
_____
_____
_____
_____
_____
_____
_____
_____

ACTIVE

thursday

Date:

Daily affirmations

I AM _____

I AM _____

I AM _____

I AM _____

Grateful for

_____

_____

_____

_____

daily check in

I feel:

I need:

Inspiration:

Song:

WHAT I LIKE
ABOUT MY
SELF TODAY?

Word Of the Week

active

WHO DO I KNOW IS THE BEST AT THIS? WHY?

_____

_____

_____

_____

_____

_____

_____

ACTIVE

friday

Date:

Daily affirmations

I AM _____

I AM _____

I AM _____

I AM _____

Grateful for

_____

_____

_____

_____

_____

daily check in

I feel:

I need:

Inspiration:

Song:

WHAT I LIKE
ABOUT MY
SELF TODAY?

Word Of the Week

active

WHAT WOULD MY FUTURE LOOK LIKE IF I DID MORE OF
THIS WORD EACH DAY?

_____

_____

_____

_____

_____

_____

_____

_____

_____

ACTIVE

weekend

Date:

Daily affirmations

I AM _____

I AM _____

I AM _____

I AM _____

Grateful for

_____
_____
_____
_____

daily check in

I feel:

I need:

Inspiration:

Song:

WHAT I LIKE
ABOUT MY
SELF TODAY?

Word Of the Week

active
REFLECTIONS

_____
_____
_____
_____
_____
_____
_____
_____
_____

ACTIVE

Notes

monday

Date:

Daily affirmations

I AM _____

I AM _____

I AM _____

I AM _____

Grateful for

_____

_____

_____

_____

_____

daily check in

I feel:

I need:

Inspiration:

Song:

WHAT I LIKE
ABOUT MY
SELF TODAY?

Word Of the Week

wealthy

THIS WEEK, HOW CAN I EMBODY THIS WORD?

_____

_____

_____

_____

_____

_____

_____

WEALTHY

tuesday

Date:

Daily affirmations

I AM _____

I AM _____

I AM _____

I AM _____

Grateful for

_____

_____

_____

_____

daily check in

I feel:

I need:

Inspiration:

Song:

WHAT I LIKE
ABOUT MY
SELF TODAY?

Word Of the Week

wealthy

HOW WOULD I DEFINE THIS WORD?

_____

_____

_____

_____

_____

_____

_____

_____

_____

WEALTHY

wednesday

Date:

Daily affirmations

I AM _____
I AM _____
I AM _____
I AM _____

Grateful for

_____
_____
_____
_____
_____

daily check in

I feel:

I need:

Inspiration:

Song:

WHAT I LIKE
ABOUT MY
SELF TODAY?

Word Of the Week

wealthy

LIST WAYS I HAVE BEEN THIS WORD IN THE PAST AND PRESENT?

_____
_____
_____
_____
_____
_____
_____
_____
_____
_____

WEALTHY

thursday

Date:

Daily affirmations

I AM _____

I AM _____

I AM _____

I AM _____

Grateful for

_____
_____
_____
_____

daily check in

I feel:

I need:

Inspiration:

Song:

WHAT I LIKE ABOUT MY SELF TODAY?

Word Of the Week

wealthy

WHO DO I KNOW IS THE BEST AT THIS? WHY?

_____
_____
_____
_____
_____
_____
_____
_____
_____

WEALTHY

friday

Date: _____

Daily affirmations

I AM _____
I AM _____
I AM _____
I AM _____

Grateful for

_____
_____
_____
_____
_____

daily check in

I feel:

I need:

Inspiration:

Song:

WHAT I LIKE ABOUT MY SELF TODAY?

Word Of the Week

wealthy

WHAT WOULD MY FUTURE LOOK LIKE IF I DID MORE OF THIS WORD EACH DAY?

_____
_____
_____
_____
_____
_____
_____
_____
_____

WEALTHY

 *weekend*

Date:

Daily affirmations

I AM _____
I AM _____
I AM _____
I AM _____

Grateful for

_____
_____
_____
_____

daily check in

I feel:

I need:

Inspiration:

Song:

WHAT I LIKE ABOUT MY SELF TODAY?

Word Of the Week

wealthy

REFLECTIONS

_____
_____
_____
_____
_____
_____
_____
_____
_____
_____

WEALTHY

Notes

monday

Date:

Daily affirmations

I AM _____
I AM _____
I AM _____
I AM _____

Grateful for

_____
_____
_____
_____

daily check in

I feel:

I need:

Inspiration:

Song:

WHAT I LIKE
ABOUT MY
SELF TODAY?

Word Of the Week

energetic

THIS WEEK, HOW CAN I EMBODY THIS WORD?

_____
_____
_____
_____
_____
_____
_____
_____

ENERGETIC

tuesday

Date:

Daily affirmations

I AM _____

I AM _____

I AM _____

I AM _____

Grateful for

_____
_____
_____
_____
_____

daily check in

I feel:

I need:

Inspiration:

Song:

WHAT I LIKE
ABOUT MY
SELF TODAY?

Word Of the Week

energetic

HOW WOULD I DEFINE THIS WORD?

_____
_____
_____
_____
_____
_____
_____
_____
_____
_____

ENERGETIC

wednesday

Date:

Daily affirmations

I AM _____
I AM _____
I AM _____
I AM _____

Grateful for

_____
_____
_____
_____

daily check in

I feel:

I need:

Inspiration:

Song:

WHAT I LIKE ABOUT MY SELF TODAY?

Word Of the Week

energetic

LIST WAYS I HAVE BEEN THIS WORD IN THE PAST AND PRESENT?

_____
_____
_____
_____
_____
_____
_____
_____
_____
_____

ENERGETIC

thursday

Date:

Daily affirmations

I AM _____
I AM _____
I AM _____
I AM _____

Grateful for

_____
_____
_____
_____

daily check in

I feel:

I need:

Inspiration:

Song:

WHAT I LIKE
ABOUT MY
SELF TODAY?

Word Of the Week

energetic

WHO DO I KNOW IS THE BEST AT THIS? WHY?

_____
_____
_____
_____
_____
_____
_____
_____
_____
_____

ENERGETIC

friday

Date:

Daily affirmations

I AM _____
I AM _____
I AM _____
I AM _____

Grateful for

_____
_____
_____
_____

daily check in

I feel:

I need:

Inspiration:

Song:

WHAT I LIKE ABOUT MY SELF TODAY?

Word Of the Week

energetic

WHAT WOULD MY FUTURE LOOK LIKE IF I DID MORE OF THIS WORD EACH DAY?

_____
_____
_____
_____
_____
_____
_____
_____
_____
_____
_____

ENERGETIC

weekend

Date:

Daily affirmations

I AM _____

I AM _____

I AM _____

I AM _____

Grateful for

_____

_____

_____

_____

daily check in

I feel:

I need:

Inspiration:

Song:

WHAT I LIKE
ABOUT MY
SELF TODAY?

Word Of the Week

energetic

REFLECTIONS

_____

_____

_____

_____

_____

_____

_____

_____

_____

ENERGETIC

Notes

monday

Date: _____

Daily affirmations

I AM _____

I AM _____

I AM _____

I AM _____

Grateful for

_____

_____

_____

_____

_____

daily check in

I feel:

I need:

Inspiration:

Song:

WHAT I LIKE
ABOUT MY
SELF TODAY?

Word Of the Week

peaceful

THIS WEEK, HOW CAN I EMBODY THIS WORD?

_____

_____

_____

_____

_____

_____

_____

_____

_____

_____

PEACEFUL

tuesday

Date:

Daily affirmations

I AM _____

I AM _____

I AM _____

I AM _____

Grateful for

_____

_____

_____

_____

_____

daily check in

I feel:

I need:

Inspiration:

Song:

WHAT I LIKE
ABOUT MY
SELF TODAY?

Word Of the Week

peaceful

HOW WOULD I DEFINE THIS WORD?

_____
_____
_____
_____
_____
_____
_____
_____
_____
_____

PEACEFUL

wednesday

Date: _____

Daily affirmations

I AM _____
I AM _____
I AM _____
I AM _____

Grateful for

_____
_____
_____
_____
_____

daily check in

I feel:

I need:

Inspiration:

Song:

WHAT I LIKE
ABOUT MY
SELF TODAY?

Word Of the Week

peaceful

LIST WAYS I HAVE BEEN THIS WORD IN THE PAST AND
PRESENT?

_____
_____
_____
_____
_____
_____
_____
_____

PEACEFUL

thursday

Date:

Daily affirmations

I AM _____
I AM _____
I AM _____
I AM _____

Grateful for

_____
_____
_____
_____

daily check in

I feel:

I need:

Inspiration:

Song:

WHAT I LIKE ABOUT MY SELF TODAY?

Word Of the Week

peaceful

WHO DO I KNOW IS THE BEST AT THIS? WHY?

_____
_____
_____
_____
_____
_____
_____
_____
_____

PEACEFUL

friday

Date: _____

Daily affirmations

I AM _____
I AM _____
I AM _____
I AM _____

Grateful for

_____
_____
_____
_____
_____

daily check in

I feel:

I need:

Inspiration:

Song:

WHAT I LIKE ABOUT MY SELF TODAY?

Word Of the Week

peaceful

WHAT WOULD MY FUTURE LOOK LIKE IF I DID MORE OF THIS WORD EACH DAY?

_____
_____
_____
_____
_____
_____
_____
_____
_____

PEACEFUL

weekend

Date:

Daily affirmations

I AM _____

I AM _____

I AM _____

I AM _____

Grateful for

_____

_____

_____

_____

_____

daily check in

I feel:

I need:

Inspiration:

Song:

WHAT I LIKE ABOUT MY SELF TODAY?

Word Of the Week

peaceful

REFLECTIONS

_____

_____

_____

_____

_____

_____

_____

_____

_____

_____

PEACEFUL

Notes

monday

Date:

Daily affirmations

I AM _____

I AM _____

I AM _____

I AM _____

Grateful for

_____

_____

_____

_____

_____

daily check in

I feel:

I need:

Inspiration:

Song:

WHAT I LIKE
ABOUT MY
SELF TODAY?

Word Of the Week

empowering

THIS WEEK, HOW CAN I EMBODY THIS WORD?

_____
_____
_____
_____
_____
_____
_____
_____
_____

EMPOWERING

tuesday

Date:

Daily affirmations

I AM _____

I AM _____

I AM _____

I AM _____

Grateful for

_____
_____
_____
_____
_____

daily check in

I feel:

I need:

Inspiration:

Song:

WHAT I LIKE
ABOUT MY
SELF TODAY?

Word Of the Week

empowering

HOW WOULD I DEFINE THIS WORD?

_____
_____
_____
_____
_____
_____
_____
_____
_____
_____

EMPOWERING

wednesday

Date:

Daily affirmations

I AM _____
I AM _____
I AM _____
I AM _____

Grateful for

_____
_____
_____
_____

daily check in

I feel:

I need:

Inspiration:

Song:

WHAT I LIKE ABOUT MY SELF TODAY?

Word Of the Week

empowering

LIST WAYS I HAVE BEEN THIS WORD IN THE PAST AND PRESENT?

_____
_____
_____
_____
_____
_____
_____
_____
_____
_____

EMPOWERING

thursday

Date:

Daily affirmations

I AM _____

I AM _____

I AM _____

I AM _____

Grateful for

_____

_____

_____

_____

_____

daily check in

I feel:

I need:

Inspiration:

Song:

WHAT I LIKE
ABOUT MY
SELF TODAY?

Word Of the Week

empowering

WHO DO I KNOW IS THE BEST AT THIS? WHY?

_____

_____

_____

_____

_____

_____

_____

_____

_____

EMPOWERING

friday

Date:

Daily affirmations

I AM _____

I AM _____

I AM _____

I AM _____

Grateful for

_____

_____

_____

_____

_____

daily check in

I feel:

I need:

Inspiration:

Song:

WHAT I LIKE ABOUT MY SELF TODAY?

Word Of the Week

empowering

WHAT WOULD MY FUTURE LOOK LIKE IF I DID MORE OF THIS WORD EACH DAY?

_____

_____

_____

_____

_____

_____

_____

_____

_____

_____

EMPOWERING

weekend

Date:

Daily affirmations

I AM _____
I AM _____
I AM _____
I AM _____

Grateful for

_____
_____
_____
_____

daily check in

I feel:

I need:

Inspiration:

Song:

WHAT I LIKE
ABOUT MY
SELF TODAY?

Word Of the Week

empowering

REFLECTIONS

_____
_____
_____
_____
_____
_____
_____
_____

EMPOWERING

Notes

monday

Date:

Daily affirmations

I AM _____

I AM _____

I AM _____

I AM _____

Grateful for

_____

_____

_____

_____

_____

daily check in

I feel:

I need:

Inspiration:

Song:

WHAT I LIKE
ABOUT MY
SELF TODAY?

Word Of the Week

growth

THIS WEEK, HOW CAN I EMBODY THIS WORD?

_____

_____

_____

_____

_____

_____

_____

_____

_____

GROWTH

tuesday

Date:

Daily affirmations

I AM _____
I AM _____
I AM _____
I AM _____

Grateful for

_____
_____
_____
_____

daily check in

I feel:

I need:

Inspiration:

Song:

WHAT I LIKE
ABOUT MY
SELF TODAY?

Word Of the Week

growth

HOW WOULD I DEFINE THIS WORD?

_____
_____
_____
_____
_____
_____
_____
_____

GROWTH

wednesday

Date:

Daily affirmations

I AM _____

I AM _____

I AM _____

I AM _____

Grateful for

_____

_____

_____

_____

_____

daily check in

I feel:

I need:

Inspiration:

Song:

WHAT I LIKE ABOUT MY SELF TODAY?

Word Of the Week

growth

LIST WAYS I HAVE BEEN THIS WORD IN THE PAST AND PRESENT?

_____

_____

_____

_____

_____

_____

_____

_____

_____

GROWTH

thursday

Date:

Daily affirmations

I AM _____
I AM _____
I AM _____
I AM _____

Grateful for

_____
_____
_____
_____

daily check in

I feel:

I need:

Inspiration:

Song:

WHAT I LIKE
ABOUT MY
SELF TODAY?

Word Of the Week

growth

WHO DO I KNOW IS BEST AT THIS? WHY?

GROWTH

friday

Date: _____

Daily affirmations _____

I AM _____
I AM _____
I AM _____
I AM _____

Grateful for _____

_____
_____
_____
_____
_____

daily check in

I feel:

I need:

Inspiration:

Song:

WHAT I LIKE
ABOUT MY
SELF TODAY?

Word Of the Week _____

growth _____

WHAT WOULD MY FUTURE LOOK LIKE IF I DID MORE OF
THIS WORD EACH DAY?

_____
_____
_____
_____
_____
_____
_____
_____
_____
_____

GROWTH

weekend

Date:

Daily affirmations

I AM _____

I AM _____

I AM _____

I AM _____

Grateful for

_____
_____
_____
_____

daily check in

I feel:

I need:

Inspiration:

Song:

WHAT I LIKE
ABOUT MY
SELF TODAY?

Word Of the Week

growth

REFLECTIONS

_____
_____
_____
_____
_____
_____
_____
_____
_____
_____

GROWTH

Notes

Made in the USA
Columbia, SC
01 December 2022

72486134R00100